PIANO TOWN
Level 2 • Theory
By Keith Snell & Diane Hidy

Contents

ISBN 0-8497-7331-8
© **2004 Kjos Music Press**, 4382 Jutland Drive, San Diego, California.
International copyright secured. All rights reserved. Printed in U.S.A.

Use with *Lessons*, page 4.

Note Naming Review

1. Write the letter name of each note.
   Then, play them on the piano.

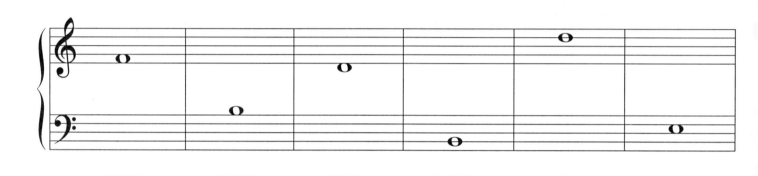

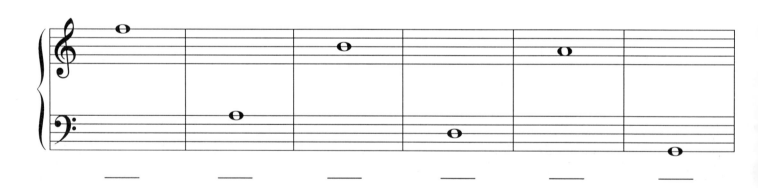

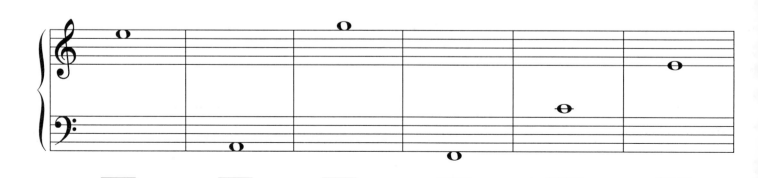

MP112

Interval Review

Harmonic Intervals   Melodic Intervals

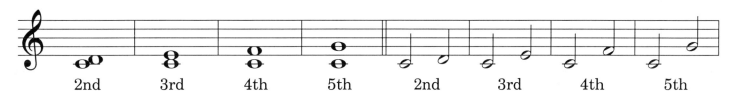

2nd   3rd   4th   5th   2nd   3rd   4th   5th

2. Write the name of each interval (2nd, 3rd, 4th, or 5th).
   Then, play them on the piano.

Use with *Lessons*, page 6 and 7.

6th

6ths on the keyboard
skip four white keys.

6ths on the staff move from
a space to a line or a line to a space.

3. Draw a half note after each given note to form a melodic 6th.
   (The first one is done for you.) Then, play each interval on the piano.

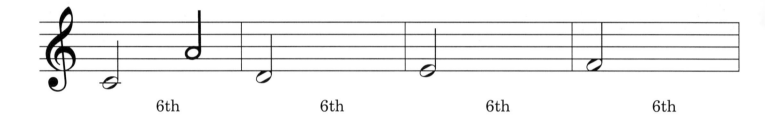

6th   6th   6th   6th

6th   6th   6th   6th

4. Draw a whole note **above** each given note to form a harmonic 6th. Play them.

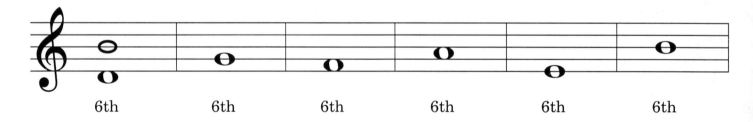

6th   6th   6th   6th   6th   6th

5. Draw a whole note **below** each given note to form a harmonic 6th. Play them.

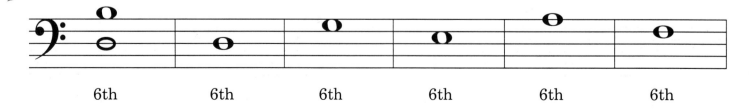

6th   6th   6th   6th   6th   6th

 MP112

7th

7ths on the keyboard
skip five white keys.

7ths on the staff move from
a space to a space or a line to a line.

6. Draw a half note after each given note to form a melodic 7th. Play them.

7th   7th   7th   7th

7th   7th   7th   7th

7. Draw a whole note **above** each given note to form a harmonic 7th. Play them.

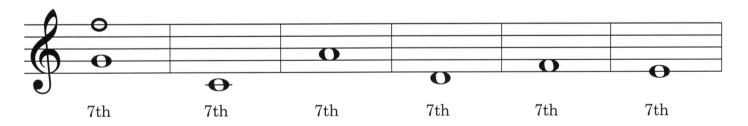

7th   7th   7th   7th   7th   7th

8. Draw a whole note **below** each given note to form a harmonic 7th. Play them.

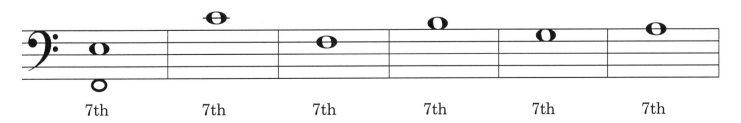

7th   7th   7th   7th   7th   7th

Use with *Lessons*, page 12.

Half Steps

A **half step** is the distance from one key to the very next key with no key between.
Half steps can look three different ways on the keyboard:

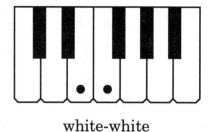

white-black   black-white   white-white

9. Draw a whole note a half step **higher** than each given note.
   Play these half steps on the piano.

10. Draw a half note a half step **lower** than each given note.
    Play these half steps on the piano.

11. Circle the half steps in this melody. There are five.
    (The first one is done for you.) Play this melody.

MP112

Whole Steps

A **whole step** is the distance from one key to the next key with one key between.
Whole steps can look four different ways on the keyboard:

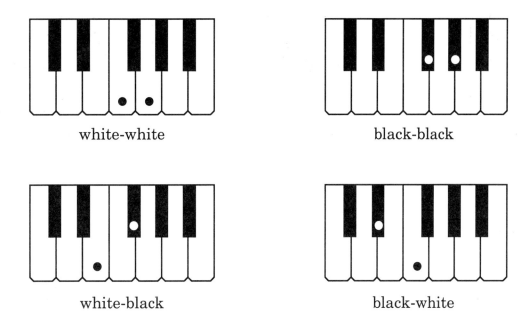

white-white   black-black

white-black   black-white

12. Draw a whole note a whole step **higher** than each given note.
    Play these whole steps on the piano.

13. Draw a quarter note a whole step **lower** than each given note.
    Play these whole steps on the piano.

14. Circle the whole steps in this melody. There are four.
    Play this melody.

LH 5

Use with *Lessons*, page 16 and 17.

C Major Scale

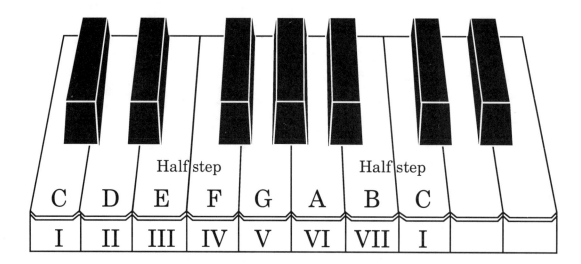

Major scales are made with half steps and whole steps in a particular order.

The half steps in a Major scale are always from III to IV and VII to I.
(Roman numerals are used to number the notes of a scale.)

In the C Major scale, both half steps are on white keys.

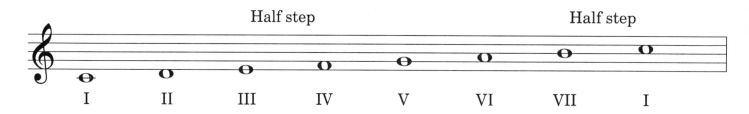

15. Draw the notes of the C Major scale going **up**. Use quarter notes.
    Circle the half steps. Play the scale with your right hand.

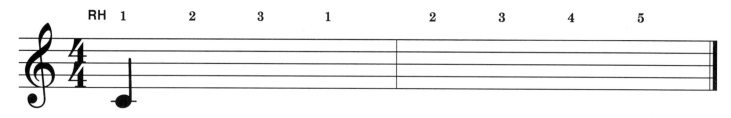

16. Draw the notes of the C Major Scale going **down**. Use quarter notes.
    Circle the half steps. Play the scale with your left hand.

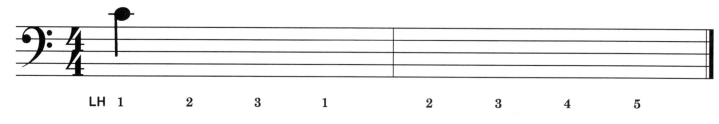

MP112

Signs and Terms Review

17. Match these key signatures.

_____ C Major

_____ F Major

_____ G Major

18. Arrange these dynamic signs from softest to loudest.

$$mf \quad p \quad f \quad mp$$

_p_ _____ _____ _____

19. Write the meaning of each term.

ritardando (rit.) _____

a tempo _____

crescendo (cresc.) _____

diminuendo (dim.) _____

Use with *Lessons*, page 18 and 19.

Primary Chords

Chords built on the first, fourth and fifth notes (also called *degrees*) of a scale
are called **primary chords**.

Primary Chords in C Major

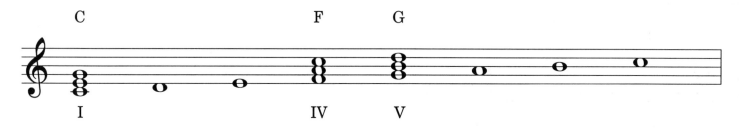

20. Draw the notes of the C Major scale. Use whole notes.
    Then, draw the primary chords.
    Write a Roman numeral under each chord.
    Write the letter name above each chord.

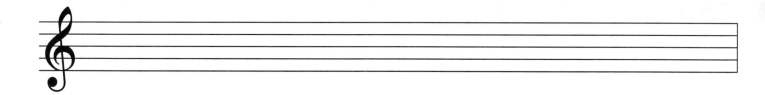

21. Draw the primary chords in C Major in the treble and bass staff.
    Use whole notes. Play them.

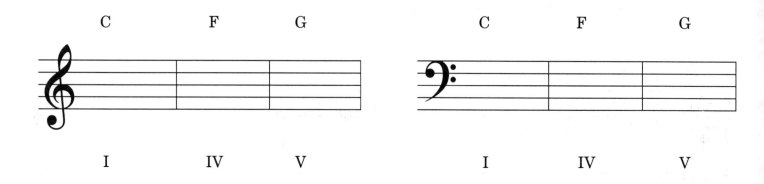

MP112

Chord Progression I - IV

Changing from one chord to another is called a **chord progression**.

To make the progression from I to IV sound better and easier to play, we will arrange the notes of the IV chord as shown below.

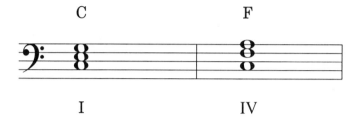

22. Draw I and IV chords as shown above. Use whole notes.
    Play these chords.

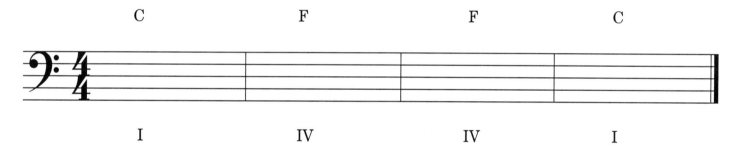

23. Play this melody and decide which chord sounds best in each measure: I or IV.
    Draw the chord in the bass staff. Use whole notes.
    Write Roman numerals below the staff.
    Write the letter name of each chord above the staff.

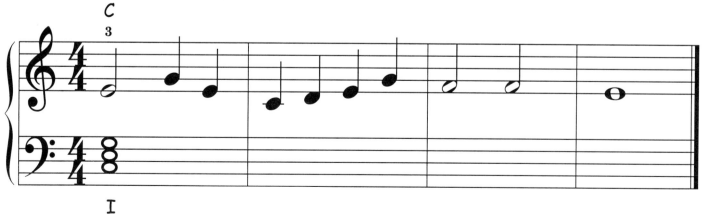

MP112

Chord Progression I - V7

The V7 (five-seven) chord is a four note chord,
built on the fifth degree of the scale.

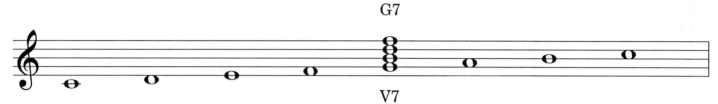

The V7 chord is the V chord,
plus the interval of a 7th:

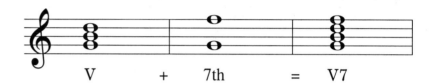

In music, one or two of the notes of a V7 chord are usually omitted (left out).
This often sounds better and makes it easier to play the V7 chord.

We will play the chord progression I - V7 with the
notes of the V7 chord arranged as shown below.

24. Draw I and V7 chords. Use whole notes. Play these chords.

25. Play this melody and decide which chord sounds best in each measure: I or V7.
    Draw the chord in the bass staff. Use whole notes.
    Write Roman numerals below the staff.
    Write the letter name of each chord above the staff.

Primary Chord Progression in C

A **primary chord progression** uses all three primary chords: I, IV, and V7.

Shown below are the primary chords as they
will be used in the primary chord progression.

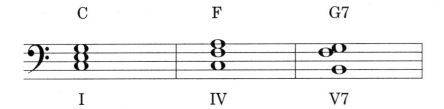

26. Draw I, IV, and V7 chords. Use whole notes. Play these chords.

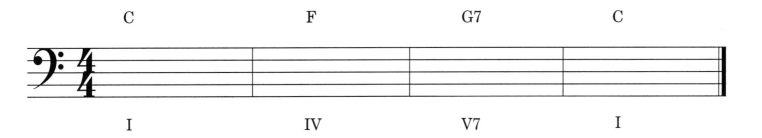

27. Play this melody and decide which chord sounds best in each measure: I, IV, or V7.
    Draw the chord in the bass staff. Use whole notes.
    Write Roman numerals below the staff.
    Write the letter name of each chord above the staff.

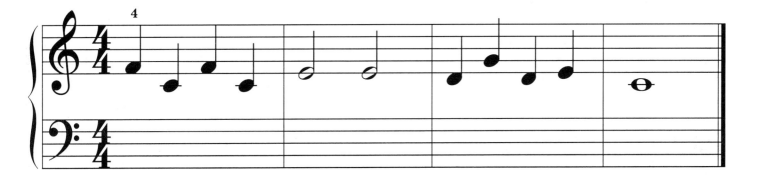

MP112

Use with *Lessons*, page 26 and 27.

F Major Scale

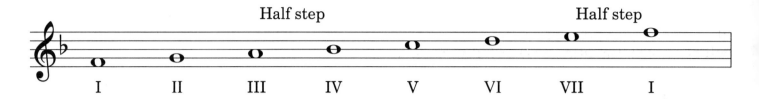

28. Draw the notes of the F Major scale going **up**. Use quarter notes.
    Circle the half steps. Play the scale with your right hand.

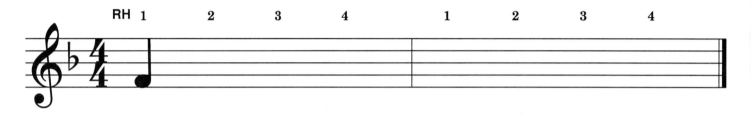

29. Draw the notes of the F Major scale going **down**. Use quarter notes.
    Circle the half steps. Play the scale with your left hand.

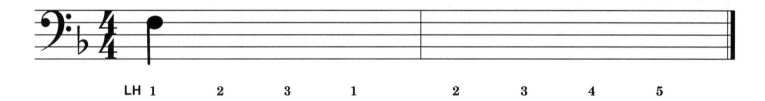

Primary Chords in F Major

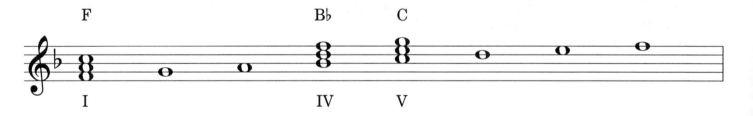

30. Draw the primary chords in F Major in the treble and bass staff. Use whole notes.
    Play them.

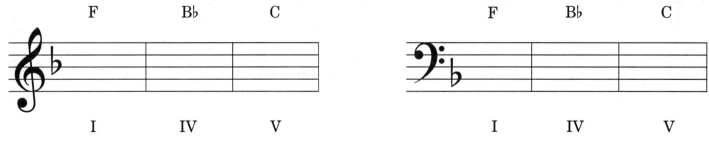

Primary Chord Progression in F

Shown below are the primary chords as they
will be used in the primary chord progression.

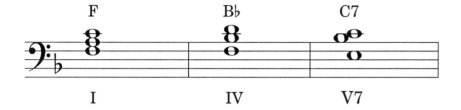

31. Draw I, IV, and V7 chords. Use whole notes. Play these chords.

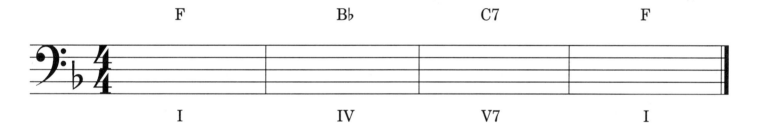

32. Play this melody and decide which chord sounds best in each measure: I, IV, or V7.
    Draw the chord in the bass staff. Use whole notes.
    Write Roman numerals below the staff.
    Write the letter name of each chord above the staff.

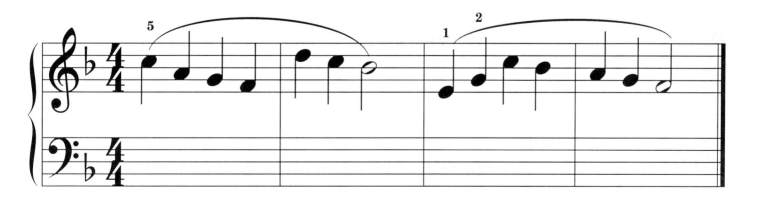

MP112

Time Signature $\frac{6}{8}$

6 means six beats in each measure.

8 means ♪ = 1 beat

♩ = 2 beats

♩. = 3 beats

♩. = 6 beats

33. Write the counts under each line of rhythm.
(The first measure is done for you.)
Clap and count aloud.

1 2 3 4 5 6

Use with *Lessons*, page 29.

Ledger Lines

Short lines can be added above or below the staff to extend the range of the staff up or down. These short, added lines are called **ledger lines**.

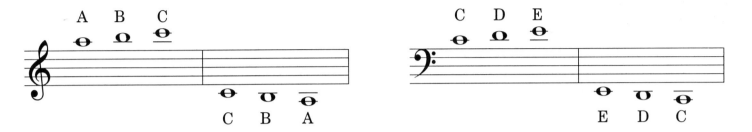

34.   Write the name of each ledger line or space note. Play them.

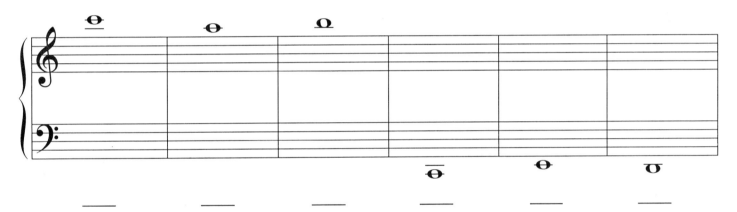

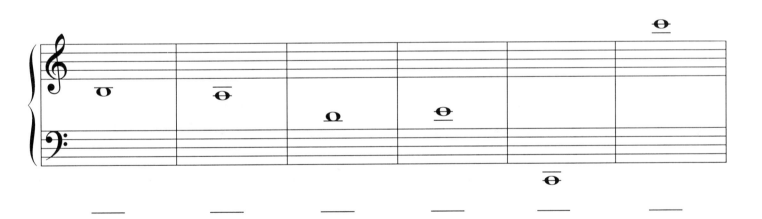

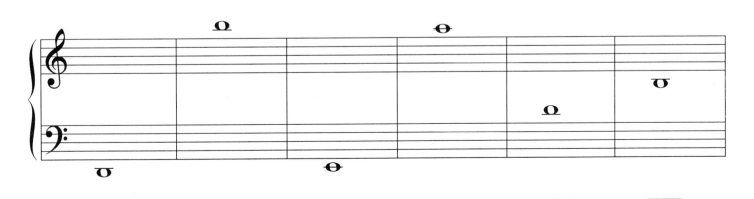

Use with *Lessons*, pages 30 - 33.

G Major Scale

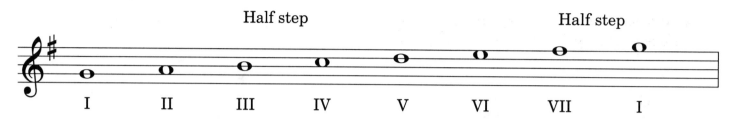

35. Draw the notes of the G Major scale going **up**. Use quarter notes.
    Circle the half steps. Play the scale with your right hand.

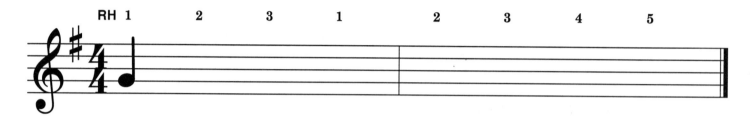

36. Draw the notes of the G Major scale going **down**. Use quarter notes.
    Circle the half steps. Play the scale with your left hand.

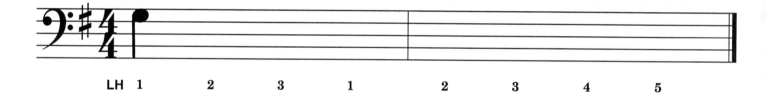

Primary Chords in G Major

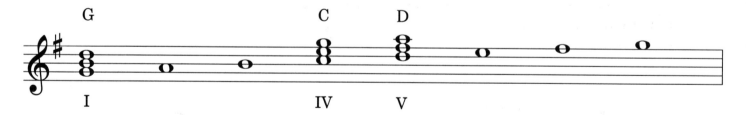

37. Draw the primary chords in G Major in the treble and bass staff.
    Use whole notes. Play them.

MP112

Primary Chord Progression in G

Shown below are the primary chords as they
will be used in the primary chord progression.

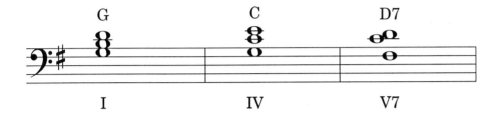

38. Draw I, IV, and V7 chords. Use whole notes. Play these chords.

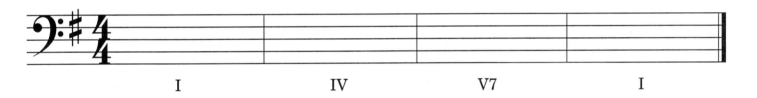

39. Play this melody and decide which chord sounds best in each measure: I, IV, or V7.
    Draw the chord in the bass staff. Use dotted half notes.
    Write Roman numerals below the staff.
    Write the letter name of each chord above the staff.

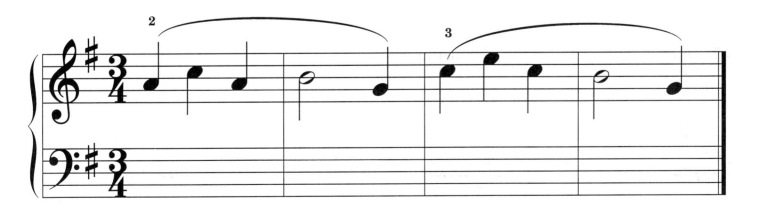

MP112

19

Use with *Lessons*, page 34 and 35.

Minor Five-Finger Positions

Any Major five-finger position becomes **minor**
when you lower the third note one half step.

C Minor   F Minor   G Minor

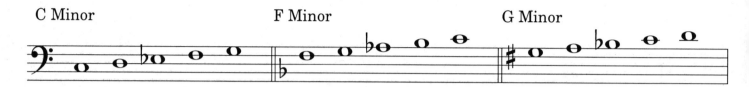

40. Change these Major five-finger positions to minor by drawing flat signs
    before the third note in each measure in both the treble and bass staff.
    Then, play each minor five-finger position.

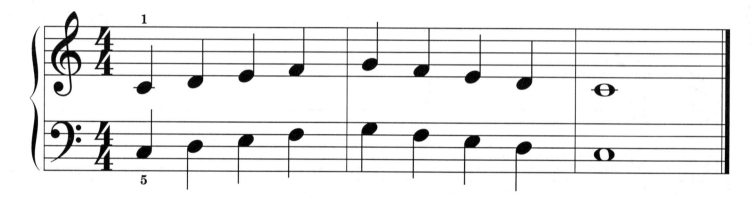

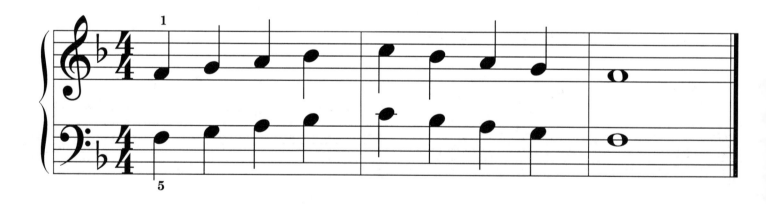

20

Use with *Lessons*, page 34 and 35.

Minor Chords

Any Major chord becomes **minor** when
you lower the middle note one half step.

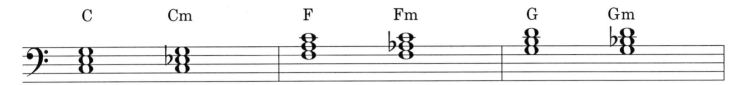

41. Draw a minor chord after each Major chord.
    Use whole notes. Play these chords.

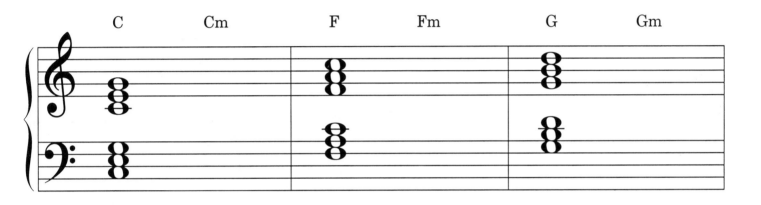

42. Play and name each chord. (The first two are named for you.)

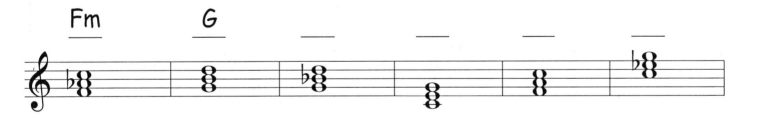

MP112

D Major Key Signature

The key signature for D Major has two sharps: F♯ and C♯.

43. Trace the first key signature, then draw two more.

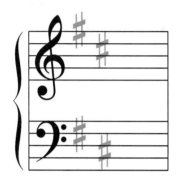  

D Major Scale

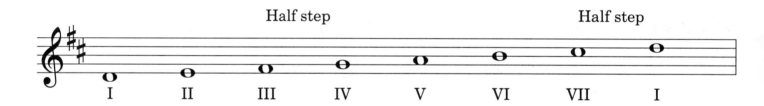

44. Draw the notes of the D Major scale going **up**. Use quarter notes.
    Circle the half steps. Play the scale with your right hand.

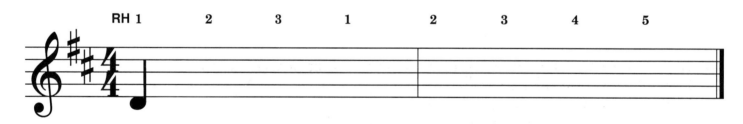

45. Draw the notes of the D Major scale going **down**. Use quarter notes.
    Circle the half steps. Play the scale with your left hand.

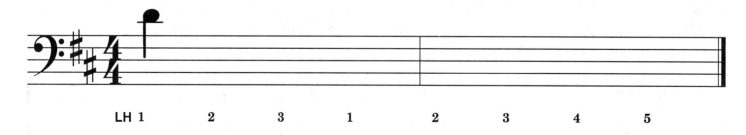

MP112

Primary Chords in D Major

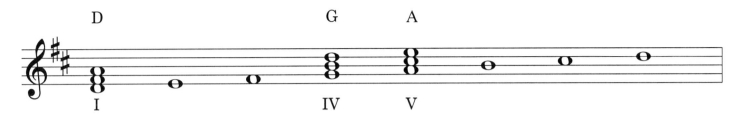

46. Draw the primary chords in D Major in the treble and bass staff.
    Use whole notes. Play them.

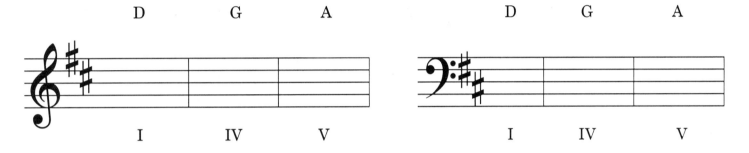

Primary Chord Progression in D

Shown below are the primary chords as they
will be used in the primary chord progression.

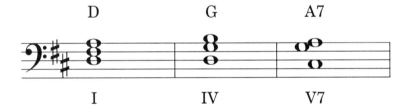

47. Play this melody and decide which chord sounds best in each measure: I, IV, or V7.
    Draw the chord in the bass staff. Use half notes.
    Write Roman numerals below the staff.
    Write the letter name of each chord above the staff.

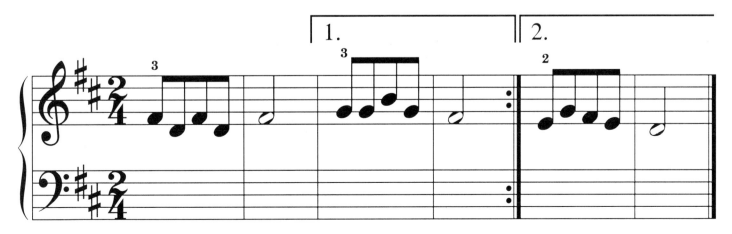

MP112

23

Use with *Lessons*, pages 40 - 43.

A Major Key Signature

The key signature for A Major has three sharps: F♯, C♯ and G♯.

48. Trace the first key signature, then draw two more.

A Major Scale

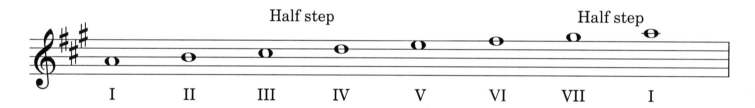

49. Draw the notes of the A Major scale going **up**. Use quarter notes.
    Circle the half steps. Play the scale with your right hand.

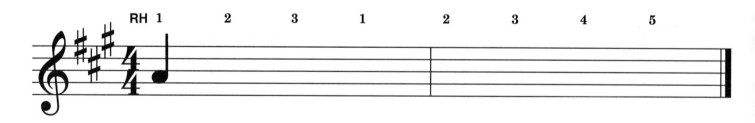

50. Draw the notes of the A Major scale going **down**. Use quarter notes.
    Circle the half steps. Play the scale with your left hand.

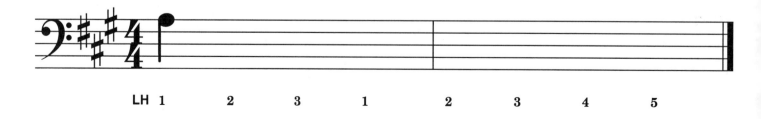

MP112

Use with *Lessons*, pages 40 - 43.

Primary Chords in A Major

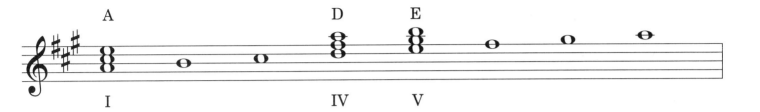

51. Draw the primary chords in A Major in the treble and bass staff.
    Use whole notes. Play them.

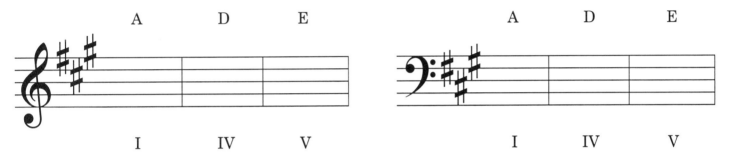

Primary Chord Progression in A

Shown below are the primary chords as they
will be used in the primary chord progression.

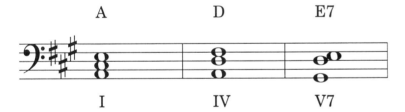

52. Play this melody and decide which chord sounds best in each measure: I, IV, or V7.
    Draw the chord in the bass staff. Use dotted half notes.
    Write Roman numerals below the staff.
    Write the letter name of each chord above the staff.

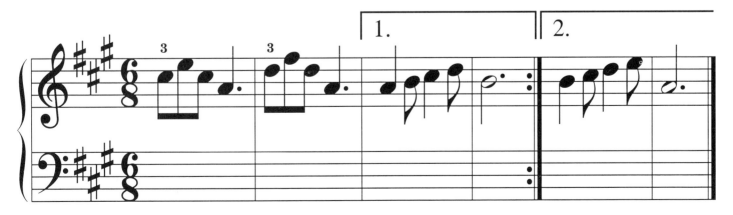

Use with *Lessons*, pages 44 - 47.

E Major Key Signature

The key signature for E Major has four sharps: F♯, C♯, G♯ and D♯.

53. Trace the first key signature, then draw two more.

E Major Scale

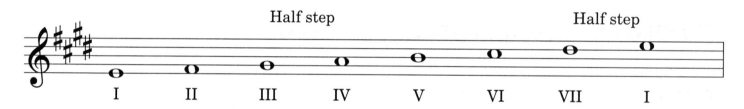

54. Draw the notes of the E Major scale going **up**. Use quarter notes.
    Circle the half steps. Play the scale with your right hand.

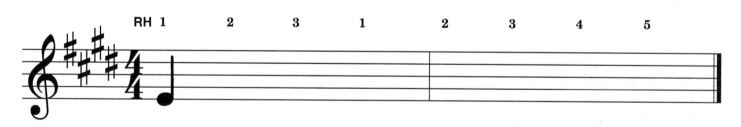

55. Draw the notes of the E Major scale going **down**. Use quarter notes.
    Circle the half steps. Play the scale with your left hand.

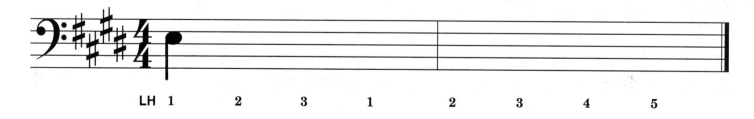

MP112

Primary Chords in E Major

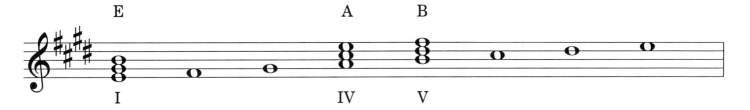

56. Draw the primary chords in E Major in the treble and bass staff.
    Use whole notes. Play them.

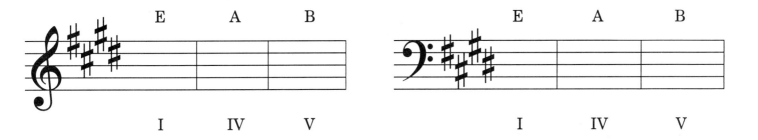

Primary Chord Progression in E

Shown below are the primary chords as they
will be used in the primary chord progression.

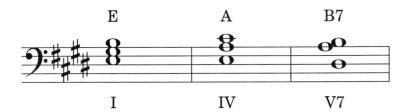

57. Play this melody and decide which chord sounds best in each measure: I, IV, or V7.
    Draw the chord in the bass staff. Use half notes.
    Write Roman numerals below the staff.
    Write the letter name of each chord above the staff.

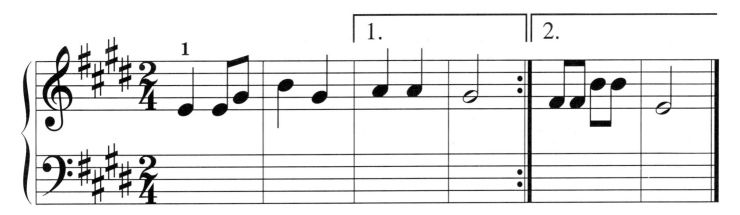

The Order of Sharps

The sharps in key signatures are always in the same order.

Memorize the order of sharps.

F C G D A E B

58. Trace the order of sharps in the first measure, then draw the order of sharps five more times.

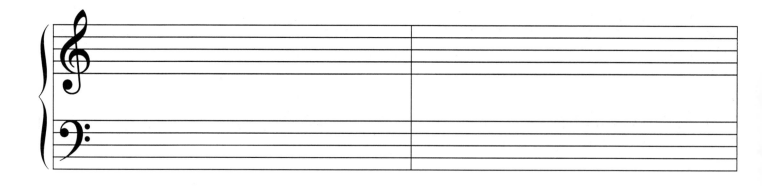

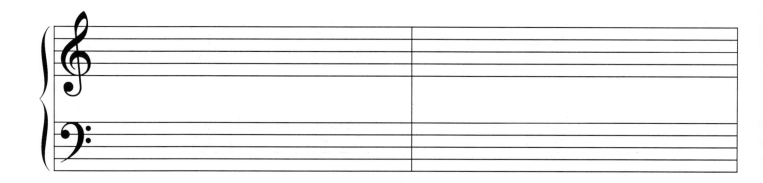

Major Sharp Key Signatures

There are seven Major keys that have sharps in the key signature. You have learned four of these keys: G, D, A and E. The remaining Major sharp keys are B, F♯ and C♯.

To recognize and name any Major sharp key signature, follow these two steps:

1. Name the last sharp (to the right) in the key signature.

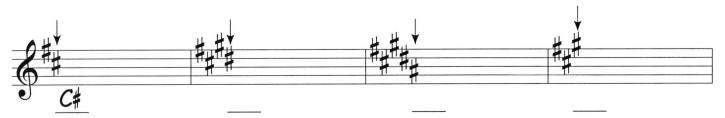

2. Name the next letter up in the music alphabet (go up a half step).
    This is the name of the Major sharp key.

59. Write the name of these Major sharp key signatures.

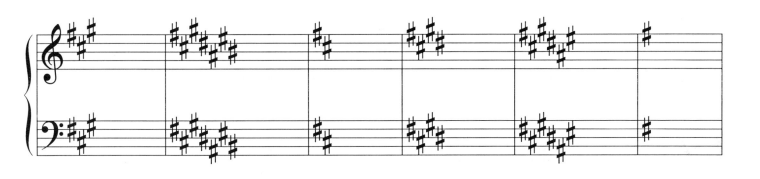

Review Test

60. Name these intervals (2nd, 3rd, 4th, 5th, 6th or 7th).

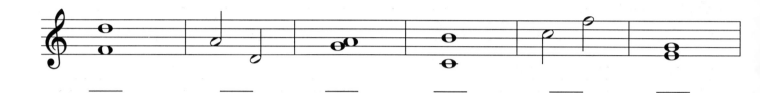

_____   _____   _____   _____   _____   _____

61. Write **H** for half step or **W** for whole step.

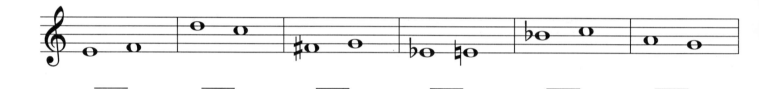

_____   _____   _____   _____   _____   _____

62. Write the counts for this rhythm.

_____

63. Match these signs and terms.

a. ⌢•   _____ crescendo (cresc.)

b. >   _____ fermata (hold)

c. ◁   _____ diminuendo (dim.)

d. ▷   _____ accent

64. Draw these Major and minor chords in treble and bass staff. Use whole notes.

C   Cm   F   Fm   G   Gm

65. Write the order of sharps in treble and bass staff.

66. Name these Major key signatures.

_____   _____   _____   _____   _____

67. Write the Roman numerals for the primary chords
and primary chord progression in C Major. Play these chords.

C   F   G   C   F   G7

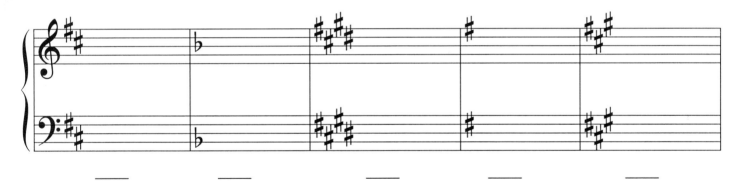

_____   _____   _____   _____   _____   _____

Music Dictionary

TERM	SIGN	MEANING
A Tempo		Return to the original tempo.
Accent	>	Play the note or notes louder.
Crescendo (cresc.)	◁	Gradually louder.
Da capo al fine (D.C. al Fine)		Go back to the beginning and play to the *Fine* (end).
Diminuendo (dim.)	▷	Gradually softer.
Fermata	𝄐	Hold the note longer than its time value.
Flat	♭	Play the very next key lower.
Forte	*f*	Loud.
Interval		The distance between two notes.
Legato		Smoothly connected.
Mezzo forte	*mf*	Medium loud.
Mezzo piano	*mp*	Medium soft.
Natural	♮	Cancels a sharp or flat.
Octave Sign	*8va--------*	When the sign is above notes, play one octave (eight notes) higher. When it is below notes, play one octave lower.
Piano	*p*	Soft.
Pianissimo	*pp*	Very soft.
Repeat signs	:‖	Repeat from the beginning.
	‖: :‖	Repeat between the pairs of dots and double bar lines.
	1. ⎸ 2. :‖ ‖	Play the first ending and repeat from the beginning. Then, skip the first ending and play the second ending.
Ritardando (rit.)	*rit.*	Gradually slower.
Sharp	♯	Play the very next key higher.
Slur	⌒	Play legato.
Staccato	⌐•	Play short and detached.
Tempo		Rate of speed.
Tie	♩‿♩	A curved line that connects repeated notes. Play the first note and hold it for the value of both notes.
Transpose		To play music in a different key than originally written.
Upbeat		The note or notes that come before the first full measure.

MP112